The TES Book of Young Poets

Illustrations by Andrew Moss

TES
THE TIMES EDUCATIONAL SUPPLEMENT

Managing Editor Patricia Grogan

Art Editor Nicola Liddiard

Editorial assistant Edward FitzGerald

First published in Great Britain in 1999 by
Times Supplements Limited
Admiral House, 66–68 East Smithfield, London E1 9XY

A CIP catalogue record for this book is available
from the British Library

ISBN 1-84122-005-1

Colour reproduction by Prima Creative Services, UK
Printed in Italy by Printer Trento

Contents

Foreword

THE FIRST TES YOUNG POET, chosen by Gillian Clarke, was published on September 8, 1994. Over 1,700 poems were submitted by Christmas that year and dozens more continue to arrive at the TES offices every week. Britain's schools are full of talent, but it takes good teaching to release it. Luckily, many hundreds of teachers are helping their students to reach the highest standards in this demanding form of creating writing and many more enjoy reading the published results and sharing in the pleasure of successful young contributors.

The purpose of the weekly TES Young Poet column is thus two-fold: to acknowledge the achievement of both the young poets and their teachers and to encourage further experiment in classroom poetry. Every week a distinguished poet experienced in leading writing workshops with young people, adds a helpful comment. The list of guests includes some of the most outstanding poets now writing, from Jo Shapcott to Michael Rosen and Moniza Alvi, from Maura Dooley to Kit Wright and Matthew Sweeney.

Choosing these few poems from the hundreds published was no easy task. In the end it seemed best to provide a collection both coherent and varied; a different set, on different themes, might have been arrived at in other circumstances. Andrew Moss' clever and charming illustrations add yet another dimension to the poems.

From the beginning, we have worked closely with the Poetry Society, and are especially pleased that Siân Hughes, the Poetry Society's education officer, herself a guest poet in 1998, has written the helpful Introduction full of yet more teaching suggestions.

We hope you enjoy this book and that you will continue to send students' poems to the TES.

Heather Neill
Arts Editor, The Times Educational Supplement

Introduction

EVERY POEM IS BOTH A COMPRESSION OF language into its most powerful and significant, and at the same time nothing more than an elaborate game with words.

Anyone who has watched children playing a musical instrument in a band, or engaged in observational drawing, or lost in a book will recognise the creative attention essential to the making of poetry. Time is suspended. The protagonist is absorbed, unselfconscious. What she or he is doing offers no greater reward than the process of doing it. Sometimes this is called 'playing'. Ted Hughes described this state as 'concentrated excitement' the purpose of which is 'to bring up some lovely solid thing like living metal from a world where nothing exists.' (Poetry in the Making. Faber and Faber, 1967) There is, of course, another kind of play, which John Holt describes in *How Children Fail* (Penguin, 1990) as 'messing about' – the kind of play that is necessary to tackle anything new, the unpressurised time for mistakes, repetitions, games, that in language emerges as jokes, songs, rhymes, catch-phrases, nicknames, slogans and slang.

Playfulness, the ability to draw on both these kinds of play, is essential to all learning, not only to poetry. It is the most neglected and central of all the core skills. It is the place where human beings are at their best and from which the best human achievements spring. But from an early age our time and our thinking are divided into work and play, and we are taught that play is less valuable than work. And once poetry finds itself on the wrong side of the work/play divide, it takes refuge on the football pitch and in the art room, in anecdote, wild conversations, jargon and codes, in graffiti and pop lyrics. That the poems in this book exist at all, is a tribute to the resilience of the human spirit, to the small corners of the school day salvaged for playfulness by inspired and devoted teachers.

A love of reading   SEVERAL OF THE POEMS IN THIS SELECTION spring from a love of reading. They reflect a reading life that is active, celebratory, and central to the poet's writing life. Jeremy Neumark-Jones' poem *Red is* includes 'A book on the horizon of my eyes' in his list of red – it is thought-provoking but not out of place among 'blood in the heart of battle' or 'A brick waiting to be built'. Words, even more than colours, can be all these things, and poetry expects no less of them. Jacklyn Kistell's poem *Mr Clarke thinks I'm reading* is a vivid account of the life of an active reader, sandwiched neatly between the first line of every stanza ('Mr Clarke thinks I'm reading but I'm ...') and the last ('In fact I'm not at school at all') just as the adventures of the reader are tucked inside the covers of the book. Robert Bowes' *All the School's a Tip* described by Philip Gross as a 'game of parody' that releases the writer from self-consciousness, is also a testament to the pleasures of reading.

Robert Bowes' line 'High on Coca Cola, faces rough like Velcro' is a piece of clear observation, heartfelt and memorable in its own right, but his poem as a whole gains energy from its model, slipping in and out of a five-beat line without fuss. One of the most remarkable things about this piece of work is the way the register of the language manages to combine a parody of Shakespearean rhetoric with high-spirited slang. The two are not so very different. Both indulge in strings of similes, Bowes' 'Smiling like loonies' and 'fighting like pitbulls' hit exactly the right note. Where the parodist hits the exact rhythm of the original, as in the line 'Their ragged jeans and leather bondage wear' he seems to speak simultaneously in both voices. This and the other poems in chapter four, *Where did that come from?* (the chapter of parodies and poems based on models) show how a young poet's voice can be released rather than restrained by following a strict format. There is no better way to get to the heart of a writer than to attempt this kind of hands-on criticism.

When an apprentice writer hears his or her own words fall into the 'correct' pattern, they will not only recognise the underlying structure of the verse, but find their own voice in terms of the one they are imitating.

Other poems written in response read more like a deliberate tribute to their original than a parody. This is not simply handing on a voice for someone else to use, it is entering a conversation. To learn a new language is always to learn to see and hear the world in a new way. Jonathan Underhill's *Rhythm of da Street* is an example of how a writer can step deliberately outside his own natural voice, in a spirit of celebration. Sprung from an enthusiasm for Benjamin Zephaniah's poetry, Jonathan's poem, like all good tributes, says 'This is what poetry is like, and I want to join in!'

Poems as tributes

THE CENTRAL IMAGE of Helen Hubbard's *For River*, in the style of Grace Nichols, that of a river carrying words from their source to the river mouth, is peculiarly suitable for a tribute poem, describing as it does, the flow of language through different ages –

River flowing in her mind
to when she felt full gorged and high
From as a trickle, to a stream
how River roared in rampant open skies

The chant-like quality of the original, its open-ended lines and flexible rhymes and half-rhymes make it an excellent vehicle for new writers. There are moments of pure imitation, dropping the definite article for instance in 'when cloud come to enclose moon', but the poem charges on under its own rhythmic energy. Was the young poet aware that she had begun her lines over and over with link-words and, from, how, when, forcing along the pace of the verse? What better answer is there to the question 'How does this work?' than simply 'Like this!'

7

Heroes and inspiration

GOOD POETS AT ALL LEVELS need heroes and standard bearers: whenever a writer chooses to write in a standard form such as a sonnet or a villanelle they are, effectively, stating a desire to 'join in' the tradition of that shape, to add their voice to that body of work, whether they are attempting to celebrate or overturn its conventions. Several of the poems collected here show how particular forms of poetry can be taught to even the youngest writers. For the less confident student or teacher, this is an ideal starting point – if you follow the rules then at the end you will know it is a poem: you will have completed a measurable task.

Haiku have long been popular in the classroom for just this reason, but the *Snapshot Verses* written by pupils of Old Hall School, Wellington, prove how the 'spirit' of haiku can be observed without imposing a strict syllable count – what matters is that the students focus on a telling moment or a precise time or place. All of these 'snapshots' work well individually and would be excellent starting points for a discussion about whether or not the strict form of 5-7-5 is any help to the reader or writer. Those who insist on a syllable count can go on to the challenge of including at least one three-syllable word, or the name of an animal, or a colour or a five-syllable noun that would work as a first or last line.

The kennings sent in by schools in Sussex show how a far less tired formula can work at junior level. Again, the students have not been restricted by the 'rules' of the poem. Ian Bollam uses alliteration throughout, Katy Daws uses similar end-sounds, neither of them sticks to a regular syllable count per line, and the poems work well both as evocations and riddles. Sarah Stringer's shape poem, *They Say We Go Round The Sun*, shows how movement as well as objects can be suggested by the shape of the words on the page, and perhaps more interestingly, too.

Breaking the rules

A FORMULAIC APPROACH need not derive from an existing poem or even a recognisable poetic ideal. Simple grammatical rules can work just as well. Perhaps the simplest of all these is the list. Ellie Oakley's *Cats* avoids

8

sentimentality by sticking to a simple structure, beginning each line (and each sentence) with an adjective. This could well emerge from an exercise where the class has to compile an agreed list of words to describe cats. Although written by an older poet, and tackling greater psychological complexity, Tanya Colley's *Make me ...* uses exactly the same list structure, with a new phrase for each line. Some of the things we want to say are best said simply and directly. We do not 'grow out' of poetic forms any more than we grow out of a need to calculate change when we buy milk. We learn it young and it stays useful.

Repeating lines and stanzas

THE HIGHLY SUCCESSFUL POEM *The Two Azizas* uses a similarly straightforward grammatical base to great effect, alternating statements about Aziza here and now with a phrase beginning 'At night the other Aziza'. Daniel Asiedu's poem *Remember me, mother?* uses a whole key phrase as a repeat line, starting with it as a title, and framing each stanza with it. Anyone familiar with good song lyrics knows that you don't need many good lines to make an impact, and when the message is this simple and forceful, it is pointless to look for another, less direct, way to say it. The other extreme of sophistication in list and repetition is seen in Emily Stokes' *Archway Bridge*, where each stanza builds on and repeats the one before, compressing the lines and combining the elements of all previous ones in new distortions and confusions. It is a very accomplished piece of work.

Often the impulse to write is a response to reading, or more often hearing, a good poem even though the resulting poem may have nothing to do with the one that set it on its course. Florence Kayll's poem *My Quiet Place* was a response to Walter de la Mare's *Myself* – even though the class of five-year-olds greeted the de la Mare with a long silence. It was later in the day that Florence wrote her poem. Similarly I would not have guessed that Steven Parfitt's brilliant poem about the terrors of the playground *I Feel a Centimetre Tall* came from reading Adrian Mitchell's *Back in The Playground Blues* (Adrian Mitchell's Greatest Hits. Bloodaxe, 1991). Sometimes all a potential writer needs by way if encouragement is permission to treat their own pre-occupations with seriousness. It can be enough simply to know that school dinners, playgrounds, lost teeth are suitable material.

Striking subject matter

THE ONLY POEM IN THIS SECTION that borrows the sentiments of another person, rather than its form, is Goldberry Miller's version of Jenny Joseph's *Warning*. The reason this works as a genuine personal expression as well as a good re-making must surely be that the sentiments of the original are easily shared – indeed the huge success of Jenny Joseph's poem rests largely on its subject matter. The most unexpected image of the young poet's version is the choice of the old woman's hallowe'en costume – not the expected witch (she lives in a forest and frightens children, so it looked like a foregone conclusion) but as a caveman – 'the mad missing link'. Could this be a reflection of recent newspaper articles explaining the essential role of older women in the evolution of early human tribes? Or is it a case of the rhyme leading the writer into unexpected areas?

Strict patterns

I HAVE ALWAYS ENJOYED the kind of 'messing about' and playing with words that comes from following strict patterns, whether it is singing the 'wrong' words to pop songs and adverts or re-writing great literature. It is the poet's role to exploit those moments where one code or language overlaps or ambushes another. Ted Hughes said 'That process of raid, or persuasion, or ambush or dogged hunting, or surrender, is the kind of thinking we have to learn and if we do not somehow learn it, then our minds lie in us like the fish in the pond of a man who cannot fish.' (Poetry in the Making. Faber and Faber, 1968) At its best this kind of play leads to a poem like Ruth Yates' *The Porpoise of Life*, a poem that defies the joke of its title to turn instead on the single visual pun of porpoises and vacuum cleaners. This poem is a perfect example of how poetry combines both concentration, keeping the subject of the poem firmly in sight and playfulness, taking a fresh look at reality. Children are already experts at both of these things. Once they connect their

10

confidence in these skills with the act of writing poetry, nothing can stand in their way.

Originality and authenticity

BUT NOT EVERY POET feels that it's a good idea to set young writers the task of copying from existing poems. One of the resident poets in The Times Educational Supplement's weekly column *Young Poet of the Week* described poetry teaching as all too commonly 'Here's a poem, now you go and write one like it'. The completion of the task is the end of the writing. The student has come no closer to unearthing his or her own voice or to saying what he or she wants to say. In the introduction to his term as guest poet in *Young Poet of the Week*, Michael Rosen advised teachers that 'the most interesting poems by children that I've read are not usually ones that came from copying the form or theme of an adult poem, but came from the children's own thought and talk'. For Michael Rosen 'originality' and 'authenticity' are inextricably linked: you cannot write your own truth in someone else's way. In a similar vein, Matthew Sweeney advises young writers to put into a poem only those words that they would use when talking to their best friend. The key seems to be to choose as starting points those poems that either speak directly and clearly to the young reader, or those that offer a method of them stepping creatively outside their own voice for a particular purpose.

Visual inspiration

YET BOTH MATTHEW SWEENEY AND MICHAEL ROSEN have selected poems by young people, which may well have been inspired by paintings. Looking intently at an image seems to be precisely the kind of meditative activity that can prepare a writer for poetry. In *Scream 2* the writer has not described the image at all, but rather used it as a gateway into an experience of her own. Something of the simplicity of the original, the concentration on a single instant can, however, inform the poem, as it has in Maria Smedstad's *Scream 2*, one of my particular favourites. The poet Charles Simic described poetry as 'other people's snapshots in which we recognise ourselves'. This is as good a reason to use photographs, portraits, paintings and statues as starting points as any I have heard.

11

When Matthew Sweeney chose Helen Rodney's poem inspired by Stanley Spencer's *Southwold*, he commented on how the poem borrowed some of the painting's sense of a metaphoric underworld, of significance behind every seemingly innocent detail. The discipline imposed by a painting steers the writer towards what can be observed rather than what they imagine or surmise. Young writers often want to bring their powers of expression to what they see as important ideas or issues and describing a painting on a particular theme anchors their thoughts in concrete images.

Co-operative writing

PERHAPS THE MOST EFFECTIVE SPRINGBOARD for young writers, however, is that of borrowing, trading and feeding off each other's work. Where exercises, games and reading-back are used as a regular part of teaching, there is a ready supply of lines and images. Swapping a poem backwards and forwards between two writers gives a very real sense of how the line, rather than the sentence, works as a unit of sense. Where students are used to writing co-operatively there is less chance of them feeling over-protective of particular words and phrases. *The Sailor's Wish* by members of the writer's group at Bromley-by-Bow shows co-operative writing at its best. The method of composition favoured by this group is highly unusual in that it is almost entirely focused on oral work and learning by heart, with editing and performing intricately linked. A collaborative approach to sequencing and editing has clearly played an important role in the shaping and finishing of *The Brigs of Sharperton*, where the difficulty of switching voices is overcome by all members of the group adopting the voice of one or other of the bridges.

Anecdotes and story-telling

WILLIAM KERLEY's *James Bond* poem emerged from a popular workshop formula usually called 'the furniture game'. The writers identify a particular well-known character (in this case James Bond) and then answer questions such as 'If this person were a car, what car would they be?' 'What book?' 'What kind of house?' 'What piece of furniture?' The answers must always be specific: 'What make of jeans?' 'What blend of

tea?' William Kerley has taken the details and worked them into a surreal and energetic narrative. The difference between the exercise and the poem is the difference between dribbling practice and a game of football – in order to put the first to any use, you have to know the rules of the game and you have to have some idea of what a really good match looks like. This can only come from reading or hearing other poetry.

Catie Chapman's *His/Her* poems seem similarly to have emerged from a lesson in personification – but again, the qualities personified, Guilt, Conscience, Hate, Jealousy, Malice and Sorrow have been brought together into a mini-drama, given relationships to act out between them, a storyline for the reader to re-construct. Poetry tends to work best on the fringes of narrative, somewhere in the region of anecdote and inconclusive or half-remembered incident. In order to write good poetry, young writers need to be given opportunities to practise this kind of story-telling, the kind that leads nowhere in particular or shapes an ordinary incident around an interesting phrase just for the sake of it. Poetry, like joke-telling and observational drawing can overturn the hierarchy of a class in a moment because it relies above all on a kind of non-linear logic where a quite different set of children can excel.

An important aspect of using writing games, activities and starting points like these is that neither the teacher nor the pupils should assume that they are going to lead to a fully-fledged poem every time. We do not expect every child who takes part in a PE lesson to go home and decide to be a footballer. We do, however, expect their repeated attendance and attention to improve their general fitness and co-ordination. Poetry is no less teachable and no less valuable. Several poems in this selection are clearly the results of particular writing games and set tasks and prove conclusively that good teaching leads to good poetry.

Siân Hughes
Education Officer, The Poetry Society

My Quiet Place

Florence Kayll

FLORENCE KAYLL has wandered unselfconsciously into the very heart of poetry with her response to Walter de la Mare's poem "Myself".
The subtlety of Florence's poem lies in the way the poem manages to hold in balance the image of the dresses in the cupboard and leaves hanging on the trees without one becoming more real or important than the other. From the point at which the dresses are likened to leaves, leaves and dresses become interchangeable.

Siân Hughes

THE DRESSES IN MY CUPBOARD feel like leaves. They are soft and the veins of leaves are like the dresses. I like the cupboard because it is dark and occasionally I like to hide there.

Florence Kayll

*Aged 5 when poem written at St Oswald's
Church of England Infant School,
County Durham
Poem submitted by Mrs Griffin*

My quiet place is my cupboard
I like my dresses hanging down like leaves
hanging down on my face
I put my face in my dresses
It is dark and quiet and peaceful
The leaves start tickling my nose
I laugh and jump **out** of the cupboard

I Feel a Centimetre Tall

by Steven Parfitt

BULLYING REMAINS A SERIOUS PROBLEM in schools, and recently we've heard how someone can get picked on for anything, even for eating the wrong flavour crisps. Steven Parfitt has written in response to reading Adrian Mitchell's *Back in The Playground Blues* (Adrian Mitchell's Greatest Hits. Bloodaxe, 1991). Steven's vivid and memorable poem reminds us that only the children really know what goes on in the playground. Breaktime is fine for those who are protected by their friends, but a nightmare for some, for those who feel, in Steven's words "only a centimetre tall".

Moniza Alvi

WE WERE DOING A PROJECT ON BULLYING and reading about it. A play came to the school I was at and that helped inspire the poem. I did have a little experience of bullying in my first year at school, but it was sorted out in a week.

Steven Parfitt
Aged 11 when poem written at Manford
Primary School, Essex
Poem submitted by Ms Penny Butters

Coming out to the dreaded playground

I feel a centimetre tall

for no one sees me,

no one at all,

playtime feels it will never end,

good for those with friends.

Jed is up the end,

I think I'm safe a bit,

It takes him a while to get here,

but how can I move?

I'm only a centimetre tall.

MR CLARKE THINKS I'M READING

Jacklyn Kistell

POETS NEED DAYDREAMING TIME. In fact "doing nothing" is an important activity for poets! Jacklyn Kistell has written very effectively about daydreaming in class. (We have to admit it sometimes happens!) I enjoyed the vigour of the imagined pursuits – the student is obviously having a really good time. The use of repetition gives rhythm and structure. I like the directness of this poem about fantasising, its everyday language and the glimpse of what might go on under the perfect cover of "reading".

Moniza Alvi

I ACTUALLY WROTE THIS at home, but I have written poems in class when I was supposed to be reading. I write in different ways, when the ideas come. I like football, play netball for the school and I act a bit. There are times when I'm dreaming and not there at all.

Jacklyn Kistell

Aged 13 when poem written at Castleford High School, West Yorkshire

Poem submitted by Mr J. Clarke

**Mr Clarke thinks I'm reading but I'm ...
sailing the ocean, climbing mountains,
white water rafting.**

In fact I'm not at school at all.

**Mr Clarke thinks I'm reading but I'm ...
chilling out with Oasis, having fun with The Verve,
starring in a film with Leonardo di Caprio.**

In fact I'm not at school at all.

**Mr Clarke thinks I'm reading but I'm ...
playing netball for Yorkshire,
kicking a ball with Stockport County,
scoring a try for Castleford Tigers.**

In fact I'm not at school at all.

**Mr Clarke thinks I'm reading but I'm ...
sailing the ocean, climbing mountains,
white water rafting.**

In fact I'm not at school at all.

THE TWO AZIZAS
Aziza Hussein

AZIZA HUSSEIN'S POEM has a pattern that has grown from an idea: two Azizas, two pairs of lines. The Aziza who lives here is immobile, but the dreaming Aziza can fly, swim and travel. I love the way we have to wait till the very last phrase to learn that the poem isn't only a fantasy about being more capable, it's also about a yearning for a special place. It sends me back to the beginning to read through again, thinking "Somalia", thinking London W10, thinking Aziza aged 9.

Michael Rosen

IT WAS FOUR YEARS AGO, I had only been in the school for two weeks. I really wanted to be somewhere else, in Somalia. I was missing lots of friends. I still think the poem is nice. I still go swimming, but I'm good at it now.

Aziza Hussein
Aged 9 when poem written at Barlby
Primary School, London
Poem submitted by Ms Sarah Stephens

Aziza watches Power Rangers

Every day on the tele.

At night the other Aziza goes

Flying through the sky.

Aziza likes swimming but

She's not very good.

At night the other Aziza

Goes swimming in the ocean

With the big fish.

Aziza never goes on holiday

But the other Aziza

Goes to Somalia every weekend.

RED IS . . .

Jeremy Neumark-Jones

JEREMY'S POEM IS A REMARKABLE – and rather frightening – example of what can be done· with this title. It's not just the strangeness and violence of his images that give the poem its impact, it's the relentless linking "b" and "t" sounds. It reminded me of an Anglo-Saxon riddle, in fact. Can Jeremy have been reading *Beowulf*?

Kate Clanchy

RED IS A FAVOURITE COLOUR. Some things that are red are frightening. I was playing around with words and one line led to another. I was near the end of the poem and I was going to get a book out of my desk and that went into the poem, too. I had been reading the story of *Beowulf*.

Jeremy Neumark-Jones

Aged 7 when poem written at Hazelwood Junior School, London

Poem submitted by Ms Toni Ashman

The sun boiling so hot and bright

The blood in the heart of battle.

A fox searching for the kill

A brick waiting to be built

Anger raging and roaring that curses me

A book on the horizon of my eyes

A storm striking down with eminent force.

Make Me

Tania Colley

THIS POEM CAUGHT MY INTEREST AT ONCE. Though it looks quite straightforward, and the language and structure are certainly clear and direct, every line is surprising. It is a series of oppositions, but not opposites. My favourite is "I am a flake of snow, make me the snow queen". We know that snowflakes are unique and beautiful, so it isn't merely a negative to positive wishing.

The device of moving from indefinite to definite article is the key to why the poem makes a kind of coherent sense, even when we can't be sure what each line means; she is only "a glowing star", she wants to be "<u>the</u> silver planet".

"Make me" seems almost a prayer but is feisty even so and has authority. The last line comes close to being perhaps over-explanatory, but it was a risk worth taking. The poem is confidently expressed and in places quite beautiful.

Ann Sansom

THE POEM JUST CAME INTO MY HEAD. It's about something small that wants to be big. I am ambitious. I want to be in the army, but I want to write as well. I like words: I find out what big words mean and add them to my poems.

Tania Colley

Aged 13 when poem written at Garibaldi School, Nottinghamshire

Poem submitted by Mrs B. J. Harpham

I am a glowing star, **make me the silver planet.**

I am a dirty rag, **make me the red carpet.**

I am a piece of mattress, **make me the four-poster bed.**

I am a tiny match, **make me the raging fire.**

I am a hot light bulb, **make me the flaming sun.**

I am a flake of snow, **make me the snow queen.**

I am a clear raindrop, **make me the colour-filled rainbow.**

I am a shivering small girl, **make me the powerful giant.**

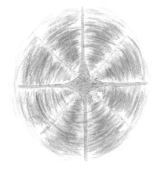

HIS-HER
Catie Chapman

I THINK HER CLASS have been working with personification – but Catie's poems go beyond an exercise to produce a particularly witty, sharp treatment of subjects which can easily become melodramatic. The poems work well as a pair, too – they enrich and complicate each other.

Kate Clanchy

THESE POEMS WERE WRITTEN as part of an exercise in personifying emotion. I wanted to get two people's points of view and all the emotions seemed to have places to go to – a pond, a street, a room. It is not necessarily about unfaithfulness. There is jealous rage, but at the end relief and regret. I remembered reading Roger McGough's poem, *Capital Punishment*.

Catie Chapman

Aged 13 when poem written at Maharishi School, Lancashire

Poem submitted by Mr C. Yates

Guilt was sitting by a pond
throwing stones into dark water.

Conscience sat beside her
and chewed its nails.

Hate came in.
She gave me some scissors.
We started a fire
and cut the heads off your photos.

Jealousy followed some way behind.
Painting the room a livid green.
We tore your clothes
and threw them out on to the street.

Malice is the fourth sister.
Stepping from the shadows in the corner of the room.
Her double-edged dagger
glinting silver in the light.

Now they are gone
and Sorrow emerges from behind the door.

They say we go round the sun

Sarah Stringer

THE RHYTHMIC CONTROL is what we notice in this poem, that and the way the poem's layout on the page mimics the spinning child. That would not be enough, however, without the control of detail – the lost feet, "the colours blend(ing) madly to green", the people twisting into space, the T-shirt that "tugs hard to be free".

Matthew Sweeney

I THINK THE POEM WAS QUITE SWEET, when I wrote it, but my style has changed a lot. I'm 20 now and reading medicine at Cambridge. It was the first thing I had published and I'm still writing. Poetry can be cathartic, but should not just be written proof of feeling; it must be something worthwhile in its own right.

Sarah Stringer

Aged 16 when poem written at St Bede's School, Surrey

Poem Submitted by Wendy Cooper

Arms out, feet lost, spinning child
    why do you spin and not stop
        when your ears turn cartwheels behind your eyes
    and your eyes are about to go pop?

Why twirl till the world is left only a blur
and the colours blend madly to green
    and the people around you just twist into space
      and the bad things are only a dream?

      You swagger and stumble, confused by the ground
    until you lie safe on your back
where the sky trips on by, and the earth rolls around
    and collapses too late to attack
      Your giggles and wobbles then tickle your toes
        and your T-shirt tugs hard to be free
      so you juggle your senses, and spin on the lawn
I wonder, will you spin for me?

CATS

Ellie Oakley

YOUNG CHILDREN LOVE MAKING LISTS in their poems and it's a useful way of encouraging their writing. In this poem by Ellie Oakley, the order of her 13 different ways of looking at cats is nicely chosen. The poem builds into a small drama moving through a number of different moods and finishing with an unusual, but precisely right observation.

Jo Shapcott

I DID ENJOY WRITING, this poem; I know quite a lot about cats. I've got three. One is called Mishka and is the son of one of my grey cats, Bel. Bel has a sister called Delphi. Sometimes Mishka is naughty and sometimes they have play-fights.

Ellie Oakley

Aged 7 when poem written at Chiswick and Bedford Preparatory School, London

Poem submitted by Catherine Jennings

30

Playful cat playing with a ball of wool.

Fat cat squeezing through some railing bar.

Lazy cat sleeping all the time.

Beautiful cat, in the mirror she looks.

Dirty cat making muddy pawprints on the clean sheets.

Angry cat, spitting and hissing at me.

Scared cat hiding in the washing

Clumsy cat knocking over his bowl of water.

Hungry cat purring and rubbing me.

Wise cat choosing to walk not in mud.

Cheeky cat slipping in the house and stealing my food.

Mummy cat cleaning her kittens.

Lonely cat sitting by herself.

Charles Sekwalor is a Monster

Charles Sekwalor

I PARTICULARLY LIKE THE SINISTER fairy-tale rhymes and the surprise of 'Those eyes!'. The images are so strange and disjointed they could almost be the remnants of a lost civilisation or belief system. It looks as if this poem sprang from a writing exercise described in *Teach Yourself Writing Poetry* by Matthew Sweeney and John Hartley Williams (Hodder and Stoughton. 1997). Taking the Slovenian poet Tomay Salamun's *Who is Who* as a starting point ('Tomay Salamun you are a genius/you are wonderful...'). They suggest stepping outside self-consciousness and into 'wild hyperbolic territory". What's the point of poetry if we can't break out of our everyday language and feast on our own grotesque?

Siân Hughes

I WROTE THIS in a workshop with the poet Jo Shapcott on World Book Day. I wanted to show the bad side to everything in the imaginary version of me first, then put in a bit of the human side. Eating McDonalds and washing hands are normal – but the fingers re-grow.

Charles Sekwalor

Aged 14 when poem written at Isleworth and Syon School, Middlesex

Poem submitted by Mr Paul McLoughlin

Charles Sekwalor is a Monster

He is a dark toe rag dark as a stomach's
    inside.

His hands are as dried as a carrier bag that's
        been used over and over again.
        Those eyes!

He has eyes that burn in the reflection of the
    sun.

Charles Sekwalor is a monster that crawls on
    his long sharp nails.

He likes to bite off his fingers which appear
    and reappear.

He will retire for the day and stop off at
    McDonald's with human roast clinging
    to his hair.

He will submerge himself in the sea.

Whether he has learnt this or it runs in the
    blood he will wash his hands
        before a feast.

Remember me mother?
Daniel Asiedu

DANIEL'S POEM would be a very effective one for speaking aloud and would offer a number of different possibilities. You could stress the bitterness and anger, but there's also tenderness and yearning here and the character speaking the poem is not the only damaged person in it. Rhythmically punchy and concise, this is a strong and dramatic piece.

Kit Wright

DANIEL ASIEDU WAS A PUPIL at Hackney Downs School in east London when he wrote this poem in 1995. The school sadly closed down at the end of the autumn term that year.

Daniel was aged 16 when the poem was written at Hackney Downs School, London
Poem submitted by Anne Gallagher

Remember me mother?
– the child you said you loved
but gave away.

Remember me mother?
– the child you said you loved
but could not look after.

Remember me mother?
– the one who lost his mother
because she drank herself to death.

The mother I always needed
But never had.

Remember me mother?

From SCREAM 2
Maria Smedstad

MARIA HAS DONE A LOT WITH A LITTLE. We know so much from what are no more than hints - if they collected glasses "all morning", there must have been hundreds of them; if their heads are aching, they must have been drunk (ish!); if "I wouldn't meet your eyes", then something must have been going on between them; and cleaning away the fingerprints is not going to clean away the memory – a memory this poem secures anyway. All this then feeds back into the line "Empty and lustreless" which seemingly describes the glasses, but clearly also describes the writer's mood.

Michael Rosen

I STILL WRITE POETRY although I'm 19 now and at art college doing a degree in illustration. I was on an Arvon creative writing course at Totleigh Barton in Devon when I wrote this and it was about something that took place there. There was a lad I fancied – but nothing much really happened.

Maria Smedstad

Aged 15 when poem written at The Hugh Christie Technology College, Tonbridge

Poem submitted by Beth Maynard

All morning we collected cold glasses

from everywhere.

Spread all over the place

Empty and lustreless

with smudged fingerprints

to remind our aching heads.

And I would not meet your eyes.

Over soap and steaming water.

We cleaned away.

In silence.

The Sailor's Wish

Bromley by Bow Centre Young People's Poetry Group

THIS POEM WAS WRITTEN by two members of the Bromley by Bow
Centre Young People's Poetry Group, aged 10-15. This voluntary
weekly workshop is attended by students who were first taught by a
language support tutor, Sister Helen Downe FCJ, at Marner
Primary School, where English was the second language for the
majority of the children. The work carries on with the current group
tutor, Clare Horsfall. The students' continuing interest and pleasure
in poetry, their imaginative and bold linguistic approach, is a
testament to the guidance they have received.

The Sailor's Wish is a fresh, charming contemporary nursery
rhyme, written after two members of the group had crossed the
North Sea to Holland with the Ocean Youth Club in force five winds.

Maura Dooley

STACEY HARRISON AND I wrote this with other members of the group
after we went on a sailing trip in the spring three years ago. *Force
10* was poetic licence, but some people were seasick. There were
15 or 16 of us. We got ideas from each other about how the sailors
would feel. We'd been writing poetry since we were 11 or 12.

Doreen Kaima

*Aged 14 when poem written at Bromley by Bow Centre Young
People's Poetry Group, London*

Submitted by Clare Horsfall

I like a bit of wind

just a bit of breeze

enough to lift my kite

just above the trees

I like a bit of wind

a force five or ten

Enough to sail the North Sea

and not come back again.

THE PORPOISE OF LIFE
Ruth Yates

I CHOSE THIS POEM because it is playful, funny, clever and imaginatively laid out, but gains its depth from one fresh and accurate simile – porpoises really do look just like an old-fashioned bag vacuum cleaner. They are plump, satisfied-looking creatures – I expect that Ruth is right, and that they do think that achieving porpoisness is a good reason for living.

Kate Clanchy

I DO STILL LIKE THE POEM, although it was written four years ago. I like writing about animals and personifications of unusual things like cats' eyes and fence posts. Someone was talking about the purpose of life in a lesson and 'The porpoise of life' and old-fashioned vacuum cleaners came into my head. I wrote the poem really quickly.

Ruth Yates

Aged 9 when poem written at Maharishi School, Lancashire

Poem submitted by Mr Cliff Yates

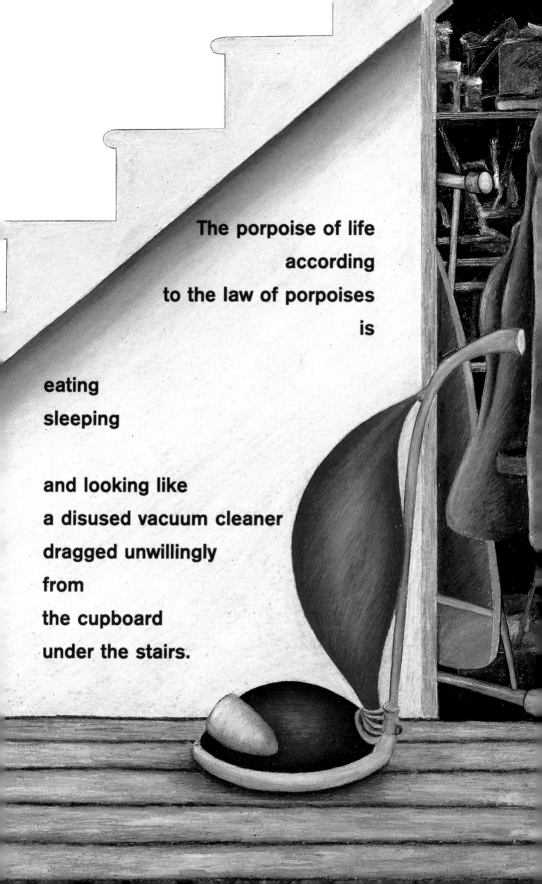

The porpoise of life
according
to the law of porpoises
is

eating
sleeping

and looking like
a disused vacuum cleaner
dragged unwillingly
from
the cupboard
under the stairs.

Southwold by Stanley Spencer
Helen Rodney

THIS IS ONE OF A SELECTION of 150 or so poems made by Advisory Teacher Annie Wright from more than 2,000 written by students in schools in North Yorkshire. Helen Rodney's poem is one in a section inspired by paintings. I like the idea of paintings being used for stimulus, as they encourage writers to trust in the visual image and leave it at that. Here, we get a clear picture of a stormy day at the seaside, with that striking and evocative final image, and in the middle of it, the wonderfully incongruous sunbathers. The whole piece is so concisely done and has the oddness and metaphoric suggestion of Spencer's paintings.

Matthew Sweeney.

I WROTE THIS when I was still at junior school; I'm doing GCSEs now, but I still like it. We could choose postcards of paintings to make into a poem. I liked the picture and I liked the idea of writing about a beach. I enjoy painting myself, but my style is quite different.

Helen Rodney

Aged 11 when poem written at Kell Bank Church of England Primary School, North Yorkshire

Poem submitted by Ms Sheila Wilkins

42

The waves toss the pebbles

Into the shore

The wet towels flap

In the wind.

The seaweed tangles round

the children's feet

The sunbathers relax

in the dazzling light.

Empty deckchairs

Rise in the wind

Snapshot verses

HAIKU IS A FORM FAVOURED BY TEACHERS. It seems simple, and its rules are easy to communicate: simply find out what syllables are and count them. The writers of these "snapshots" have managed to go beyond the syllable count to home in on the spirit of haiku, that of concentrating the mind on a single image or moment, and lending that moment a sense of heightened significance. Philippa Jemmett uses a poetic lense to zoom from the moon and stars to "here. Chloe and me.", Yuki Akazawa makes a similar leap from snowflakes to the world of human relations. These poems read as if the writers have looked through false frames or cameras in order to isolate images. This can be a starting point for any form of poetry.

Siân Hughes

WE WROTE THESE VERSES three years ago. We read some haiku and learned about their history and then we went out into the fields around the school to get ideas to write one. We had to try to stick to 17 syllables, but it didn't matter if we didn't.

Philippa Jemmett

All children aged 9 when poems written

All poems submitted by Mr Len Mullan from Old Hall School,
Wellington, Shropshire

Night
Philippa Jemmett

Far away the hills

the ice-cold moon and stars

here, Chloe and me

Geese
Samantha Powell

Above the clouds

birds like arrows

necks reaching for the sun

Winter
Yuki Akazawa

Each tiny snowflake

landing on the earth's white sheet

joining its family

Archway bridge

Emily Stokes

THIS IS A LONG, but brilliant poem – or rather, a brilliant poem because it knows just what to do with its length. All the repetitions create a haunting, frightened, slightly crazed effect – this isn't true of all repetition, incidentally, just really well-turned, fresh phrases like Emily's, which also build up tension, which is released in a genuinely surprising ending. This kind of control is unusual in any poet.

Kate Clanchy

IT WAS ABOUT TWO YEARS AGO. I was at home after an operation in hospital and often went to Waterlow Park in a wheelchair pushed by my dad. I'd always thought the bridge quite weird. People have jumped off it – it's always in the news around here. There are spikes on the railing threatening them to stop, which makes it more spooky.

Emily Stokes

Aged 11 when poem written at home in London
Submitted by Mala Perera, Home Tuition Teacher
of Islington Council, London

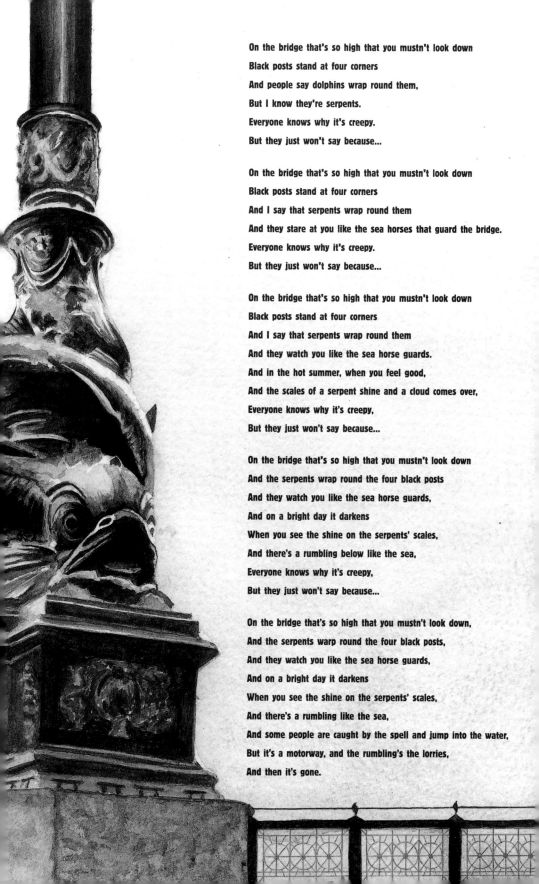

On the bridge that's so high that you mustn't look down
Black posts stand at four corners
And people say dolphins wrap round them,
But I know they're serpents.
Everyone knows why it's creepy.
But they just won't say because...

On the bridge that's so high that you mustn't look down
Black posts stand at four corners
And I say that serpents wrap round them
And they stare at you like the sea horses that guard the bridge.
Everyone knows why it's creepy.
But they just won't say because...

On the bridge that's so high that you mustn't look down
Black posts stand at four corners
And I say that serpents wrap round them
And they watch you like the sea horse guards.
And in the hot summer, when you feel good,
And the scales of a serpent shine and a cloud comes over,
Everyone knows why it's creepy,
But they just won't say because...

On the bridge that's so high that you mustn't look down
And the serpents wrap round the four black posts
And they watch you like the sea horse guards,
And on a bright day it darkens
When you see the shine on the serpents' scales,
And there's a rumbling below like the sea,
Everyone knows why it's creepy,
But they just won't say because...

On the bridge that's so high that you mustn't look down,
And the serpents warp round the four black posts,
And they watch you like the sea horse guards,
And on a bright day it darkens
When you see the shine on the serpents' scales,
And there's a rumbling like the sea,
And some people are caught by the spell and jump into the water,
But it's a motorway, and the rumbling's the lorries,
And then it's gone.

James Bond

William Kerley

THE FIRST LINE is clean and grammatical but could lead in any direction. At no stage does this poem lose its unpredictability or its sense of adventure. Poetry can free a writer from the constraints of making sense – this poet delights in eccentric line breaks and a random story line. The wildness succeeds because, although we never know what will happen next, it is always clearly described. Is "galahants" a real word, or a combination of Sir Galahad and gallivants? In any case I intend to adopt it from now on. William Kerley, like every true poet, has extended the English language.

Siân Hughes

WE WERE PLAYING A GAME where I thought of a character, then everyone asked me questions like "If you were a piece of furniture, what would you be ?" They did the same with other things- a book, a car, a meal – and wrote down my answers. Eventually they guessed James Bond and I wrote the poem.

William Kerley

Aged 13 when poem written at Maharishi School, Lancashire

Poem submitted by Mr Cliff Yates

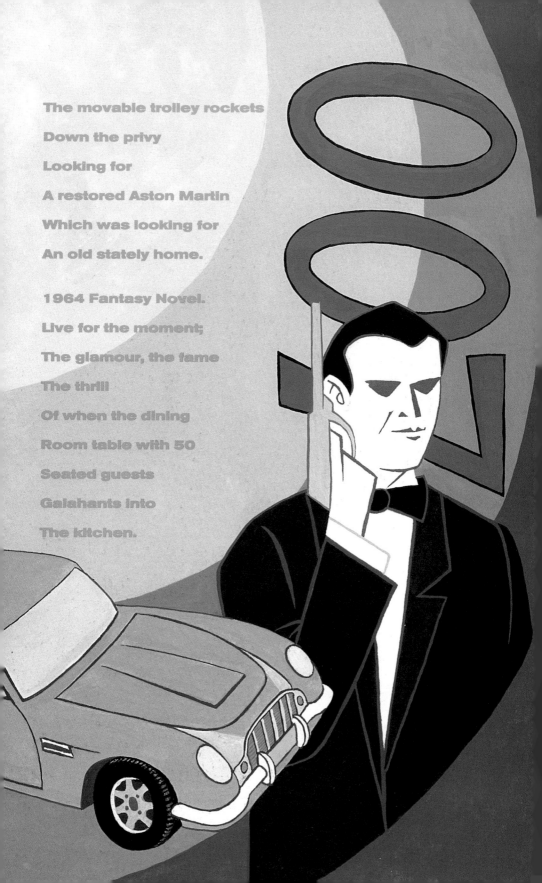

The movable trolley rockets

Down the privy

Looking for

A restored Aston Martin

Which was looking for

An old stately home.

1964 Fantasy Novel.

Live for the moment;

The glamour, the fame

The thrill

Of when the dining

Room table with 50

Seated guests

Galahants into

The kitchen.

FOR RIVER
(in the style of Grace Nichols)

Helen Hubbard

RECEIVING THIS MAGICAL POEM made a very good
start to my day. Helen Hubbard has captured
the vibrant and elemental in Grace Nichols'
style. This river, babbling along and making its
way to the sea, is not just one thing. Its journey
is one of communication and imagination, an
ageing process, mystery and beauty. Helen's
choice of language, inspired by Grace Nichols, is
strong and surprising, for instance River is a
loving mother "River carrying her children/to
her sea in firm embrace", and River is in pain
"wincing with eerie cries". The poem flows
magnificently, giving a sense of abundance and
the delight with which it was composed.

Moniza Alvi

IT'S THE ONLY TIME I've taken inspiration from
another poet. It's usually other things – recently
a newspaper article about war. I do loads of
music and that might have helped with the
rhythm. Moniza Alvi picked out the bits I liked,
the climax of it – I was pleased. I like older
poets – Shakespeare, Tennyson and Wilfred
Owen.

Helen Hubbard

Aged 15 when poem written at Monks Walk
School, Hertfordshire
Poem submitted by Carol Hedges

River could carry word
River could carry word

River babble in early morn
Word of mouth with every wave
River carrying her children
to her sea in firm embrace

But River don't seep her bank with mud
no River cover her back with blooms
from steaming jets of morning dew
and when cloud come to enclose moon
and darkness fall on her like blanket
River children go down to bed
Diamonds sparkle in fading sky

River flowing in her mind
to when she felt full gorged and high
From as a trickle, to a stream
how River roared in rampant open skies
River now at middle age wishes for those days
when her joy had not been dried
to that of old tempestuous tides
River wincing with eerie cries

and when sunbeams
wake her up with blinding light
River just creep and crawl
to a new day of thirsting love

but coming back to word
River could carry word
River could carry word
And we must follow River
to her word of mouth

MANY OF THE SCHOOLS and young poets we have heard from have been experimenting with different forms; haikus, tankus, ghazals and kennings have all been popular. The kenning comes to us from Old Norse where, originally, it was a poetic circumlocution used instead of a more familiar word. For example, banhus (literally bonehouse), meaning body. Now the form is practised using three-word lines to describe something - and often the poet presents the subject of the poem as a riddle.

Maura Dooley

WE WERE ASKED TO WRITE a poem describing something but not saying what it was. I chose a sheep because we've got lots of them. I live on a farm with 800 sheep and I help to feed them. In the winter we feed them nuts most of the time.

Katie Daws

Aged 9 when poem written at Bodiam Church of England School, East Sussex

Poem submitted by Valerie Richardson

WE WERE ASKED TO WRITE a kenning about an animal. I chose a deer because we'd been out in the copse near school and I'd seen one. I hadn't been learning about alliteration, but I thought it fitted in with the kenning – it sounded right.

Ian Bollam

Aged 9 when poem written at Bury Church of England First School, West Sussex

Poem submitted by Malcolm Laverty

A graceful grazer   A lawn mower

A high-hooved hider   A field lover

A camouflaged coward   A jumper provider

A reckless rusher   A spring indicator

A hunter's hit   A country lover

A velvet victim   A hill walker

                         A nut eater

Ian Bollam   **Katy Daws**

Rhythm of Da Street
Jonathan Underhill

JONATHAN UNDERHILL is to be congratulated on his skilful poem which reflects his recent investigation into such poets as Benjamin Zephaniah. Jonathan handles rhythm with flair and subtlety and his language has vigour. 'Changing, Ranting/Laughing, Cackling'. This poem is visually appealing with its lively pattern and movement of the page. It has a marvellous, festive atmosphere to make readers and audiences chant, dance and go in search of the 'rhythm of da street'.

Moniza Alvi

WE HAD BEEN WORKING on poems by Benjamin Zephaniah and others with strong imagery. I am interested in drama, so I didn't find the rhythm difficult. I also play the flute, saxophone and piano and am starting to write lyrics. I wanted to put into words the feel of being in a busy town street.

Jonathan Underhill

Aged 13 when poem written at Wildern School, Southampton

Poem submitted by Fiona Welch

Jump up!

Jump down!

Listen to da beat

Of da rhythm of da street

Listen to da sound
Da rhythm all around
Da beat of da beat
Of da rhythm of da street

Stomping, Stamping
Changing, Ranting,
Laughing, Cackling,
Rhythm of da street.

The Street
The Street
The street has a beat,
Called da rhythm of da street

Da rhythm of da street
Is cool, is hot!
Cum dance to the beat of da rhythm of da street
To da rhythm of da street cum dance.

The Brigs of Sharperton

ROBERT BURNS, with his democratic instincts and love of folk tradition, would have been pleased to see his 'Brigs of Ayr' used as a starting point for a collaborative exercise. Working like this, quite young students can see their best ideas taking shape together; selecting, sequencing and editing in a group is an excellent introduction to the drafting of a poem.
Philip Gross

IN 1995 A CURVED CONCRETE BRIDGE with Tuscan columns began to replace the 120-year-old iron bridge across the river Coquet at Sharperton in Northumberland. We imagined, during the transformation, what the two bridges thought of each other and wrote this collective poem.
Ms K. V. Storey

WE WENT TO THE OPENING of the new bridge and wrote the poem in groups after reading Robert Burns' poem. We tried to copy it, but make it our own. There were enough of us in our group to each have a bit of the conversation. I was the new bridge. We wrote, compared and chose the best bits.
Amanda Gilbertson
Aged 8 when poem written

Thomas Corley
Aged 8 when poem written

Ben Fenwick, Megan Hewitson, Nichola Wood
All aged 9 when poem written

Poem submitted by Ms K. V. Storey of Harbottle Church of England First School, Morpeth, Northumberland

Illustration based on a drawing by Thomas Corley

AULD BRIG

NEW BRIG

'You are spoiling my view.

You have a humpty back

and a blind spot. Your bald head

has no memories.'

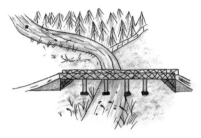

'Your rusty spikes

are like squashed hedgehogs.

You will be carried away

in a wheelbarrow and dumped

on a rubbish tip.'

'You were poured out of a bucket

like mushy peas. Your stumpy legs

are already wrinkled. Your colour

is pale as fog and you will get lost

in the dark.'

'My shape is soft and my skin

is smooth. You will die of loneliness

now that I am here. People

will come to take photographs

of me.'

'When I was young the wind

tried to blow me away. But

I was woven out of iron.

Now the winds creep through me

like a mist.'

'You are stiff as peanut butter.

You will soon disappear

like the Roman road.

Your bones will crunch

to pebbles in the river.'

All the School's a Tip
Robert Bowes

THERE IS NOTHING like the game of parody to free us (any age, but I suspect particularly teenaged writers) from self-consciousness and let something slip out which also has a tang of dangerous honesty. Riding a famous piece of Shakespeare seems to allow Robert Bowes to marshal his sharp observation into a bravura performance of real power.
Philip Gross

I'M AT LEEDS UNIVERSITY studying sports science now, but I remember it was difficult to get started on the poem, but easy once I got going. It was an exercise to help us get used to iambic pentameters. I suppose I was observant; I wasn't in any of the groups I was talking about.
Robert Bowes
Aged 15 when poem written at Fakenham High School, Norfolk
Poem submitted by Anna Lythgoe

All the school's a tip

And all the corridors and classrooms merely messy;

They have their exits and their entrances

But mobiles have a hundred holes beside

Their state caused by seven ages. At first the seventh spitting and sticking gum under the table's edge

And then the whining eighth year with his acne and bass falsetto voice.

Compassing neat holes into the window frames.

And then the ninth year.

Smiling like loonies, carving girls' names with pride into the lavatory doors.

Then the tenth terrors.

High on Coca Cola, faces rough like Velcro

Kicking in doors, fighting like pitbulls, seeking the fire alarm bell even under the teacher's glare.

And then the eleventh with their boots and manliness.

Their strength severe, rulers of the school.

Drinking away examination terrors

And so they spew in corners.

Twelfth year shifts

From kings to underdogs again,

Their ragged jeans and leather bondage wear,

Leaving old school uniforms to moulder in school shop.

Fighting for rank.

Their jangling chains scratch furrows in fine skins, staining carpets crimson

And bloodying school chairs.

Last year of all

That ends these torrid tales of damage

Is the thirteenth, horror and looming prospect

No job, no cash, no hopes, just vandalism.

WARNING!

Goldberry Miller

This is a very enjoyable piece of writing, sophisticated and self-aware, and in no way outfaced by the Jenny Joseph poem that inspired it. In fact, it seems to respond to its famous forebear, not least in the ending and in the lines about Hallowe'en, where she declines the role of witch, or wise woman, in favour of the missing human link. I like the on-the-run quality of the rhyme, and the varying metre, which owes something to the epigrammatic jauntiness of a limerick's amphibrachs and anapests. The combination of craft and amused imagination in Goldberry Miller's poem really does make it her poem, not just a classroom exercise, and a satisfying statement in its own right.

Ann Sansom

I like Jenny Joseph's poem, but that was a one-off; I don't usually write in the style of other poets. I write quite a lot, but I'm in the fourth year now and doing other things – science and art. I imagine being quite old, but fit and healthy.

Goldberry Miller

Aged 14 when poem written at St Andrew's School, East Kilbride

Poem submitted by Elaine Morrison

When I am an old woman,
I shall wrestle black bears before breakfast,
to loosen my arthritic bones.
Swim nude in the brook before sunrise.
and grow oak trees inside my home.

I'll live in the mountains and forests.
with an old wizened man at my side.
I'll go to the fairground in summer,
and scream with delight, every ride.

I'll never grow tired of popcorn,
and buy a BMX bike,
to ride all over my forests
and give trespassing children a fright.

I'll grow grass on the roof of my cottage,
and paint my walls purple and pink.
Hallowe'en? I'll dress up as a caveman,
They'll call me the mad missing link.

And when my life's nearly over,
I'll look back and think, what fun!
Yet how many years sadly wasted,
Oh, how boring it is to be young.

Poets' Biographies

MONIZA ALVI

Moniza Alvi was born in Pakistan and grew up in Hertfordshire. She has published two poetry collections: *A Bowl of Warm Air* (Oxford University Press, 1996) and *The Country at My Shoulder* (Oxford University Press, 1993). Alvi has had a long career as a secondary school teacher and now lives in London with her husband and young daughter.

KATE CLANCHY

Kate Clanchy was born in Glasgow in 1965 and educated in Edinburgh and Oxford. After graduating she trained and worked as a teacher in a variety of schools. Her first collection of poetry, *Slattern* (Chatto) was published in 1996 and won six literary awards. Her second, *Samarkand* (Picador), will be published in 1999. She has recently moved to Oxford where she works as a freelance writer and teacher.

MAURA DOOLEY

Maura Dooley won an Eric Gregory award in 1988. Her collections *Kissing a Bone* (Bloodaxe Books, 1997) and *Explaining Magnetism* (Bloodaxe Books, 1996) and her anthology *Making for Planet Alice* (Bloodaxe Books, 1997) were all Poetry Book Society Recommendations. *Kissing a Bone* was also shortlisted for the T.S. Eliot prize. Dooley worked as Centre Director for the Arvon Foundation and spent six years creating and directing the Literature Programme at the South Bank Centre. She currently works freelance and is editing two books to be published 1999.

PHILIP GROSS

Philip Gross is a poet, novelist and Point Horror author who writes for adults and children. *The Wasting Game*, (Bloodaxe, 1998) was shortlisted for the Whitbread Poetry prize in 1998. His latest collection of poems for children is *Scratch City* (Faber, 1995). Gross has also published a science fiction book: *Psylicon Beach* (Scholastic, 1998) and teaches Creative Studies at Bath Spa University College.

SIÂN HUGHES

Siân Hughes was born in London in 1965. After studying English and French at university she worked as a teacher, tutor, translator and editor before joining the Poetry Society as Education Officer. Her publications include *A Song for Carrying Water and Other Stories from Somalia* (Gatehouse Books, 1996) and *The Poetry Book for primary schools* (The Poetry Society, 1998). Her poetry has appeared in many places including in a collection entitled *Saltpetre* (Smith Doorstop, 1998).

MICHAEL ROSEN

Michael Rosen has published over one hundred poetry and prose books for children, including *You Wait Till I'm Older Than You* (Viking, 1996) and *Quick, Let's Get Out of Here* (André Deutsch, 1983). Rosen received his doctorate and won the Eleanor Farjeon Award in 1997. His research into children's literature and children's own writing has taken him all over the world. In the past twenty years, Rosen has performed his own work in over one thousand schools.

ANN SANSOM

Ann Sansom works as Writing Tutor at Doncaster Women's Centre. She has published her poetry widely in magazines, and her collections include *Romance* (Bloodaxe Books, 1994). She has held many placements in schools, most recently in Suffolk as writer-in-residence for the Aldeburgh Poetry Trust. Sansom regularly runs poetry workshops on trains with primary and secondary schools along the Penistone line between Huddersfield and Sheffield.

JO SHAPCOTT

Jo Shapcott is author of three award-winning poetry books: *My Life Asleep* (Oxford University Press, 1998), *Phrase Book* (Oxford University Press, 1992) and *Electroplating the Baby* (Bloodaxe, 1988). She co-edited *Emergency Kit: Poems for Strange Times* (Faber and Faber, 1996) and her work features in *Penguin Modern Poets 12* (Penguin, 1997). Shapcott is the current Northern Arts Literary Fellow.

MATTHEW SWEENEY

Matthew Sweeney was born in Donegal in 1952. His most recent poetry publications include *The Bridal Suite* (Cape, 1997), *Penguin Modern Poets 12* (Penguin, 1997), and for children *Fatso in the Red Suit* (Faber, 1995). Sweeney is co-editor of the anthologies *Beyond Bedlam* (Anvil Press, 1997) and *Emergency Kit* (Faber, 1996) and co-author of *Writing Poetry* (Teach Yourself Books, 1997). He is currently working on a new collection of poems.

KIT WRIGHT

Born in Kent in 1944, Kit Wright is a poet, short story writer and children's author. His books of verse for children include *Great Snakes!* (Viking, 1994), *Cat Among the Pigeons* (Viking Kestrel, 1987), *Hot Dog* (Kestrel, 1981), and the picture books *Dolphinella* (André Deutsch, 1995) and *Tigerella* (Viking Kestrel, 1993). Wright has received many prizes for literature, including in 1989 the Hawthornden Prize.

Index

Times Educational Supplement would like to thank the following children for permission to reproduce their poems in this book:
page 44 Yuki Akazawa *Winter* © 1996; page 52 Ian Bollam *Deer* © 1996; page 58 Robert Bowes *All the School's a Tip* © 1996; page 38 Bromley by Bow Centre Young People's Poetry Group *The Sailor's Wish* © 1996; page 30 Ellie Oakley *Cats* © 1997; page 26 Catie Chapman *His-Her* © 1997; page 24 Tania Colley *Make Me* © 1998; page 56 Thomas Corley, Amanda Gilberton, Ben Fenwick, Megan Hewitson, Nicholas Wood *The Brigs of Sharperton* © 1996; page 52 Katy Daws *Sheep* © 1996; page 54; page 50 Helen Hubbard *For River* © 1998; page 20 Aziza Hussein *The Two Azizas* © 1995; page 44 Philippa Jemmett *Night* © 1996; page 14 Florence Kayll © 1998 *My Quiet Place*; page 48 William Kerley *James Bond* © 1998; page 18 Jacklyn Kistell *Mr Clarke thinks I'm reading* © 1998; page 60 Goldberry Miller *Warning!* © 1996; page 22 Jeremy Neumark-Jones *Red Is* © 1997; page 16 Stephen Parfitt *I feel a centimetre tall* ©, 1998; page 44 Smantha Powell *Geese* © 1996; page 42 Helen Rodney *Southwold by Stanley Spencer* © 1995; page 62 Charles Sekwalor *Charles Sekwalor is a Monster* © 1998;page 46 Emily Stokes *Archway Bridge* © 1997; page 28 Sarah Stringer *They Say We Go Round the Sun* © 1995; page 54 Jonathan Underhill *Rhythm of da Street!* © 1998; page 40 Ruth Yates *The Porpoise of Life* © 1997

The publishers apologise for the few instances in which we have been unable to make contact with the copyright holders, and we would be grateful if they would contact the publishers.

The publishers would like to thank Helen Stone and Colette O'Neill for editorial assistance.